Letterland

Contents

Hello 2-4
Sing and move! 2
My name 5

Part 1 Sound Discrimination
Environmental Sounds - Animal noises
Listen and point! 6
Listen and stick! 7
Sing and move! 8
Drum or clap! 9
Circle time 10
Rhyme time! 11
Write-in activities 12-15
Environmental Sounds - Outdoor noises
Listen and point! 16
Listen and stick! 17
Sing and move! 18
Drum or clap! 19
Circle time 20
Rhyme time! 21
Write-in activities 22-25

Part 2 Sound Discrimination - Instruments
Numbers 1-6 My age 26
Listen and point! 27
Listen and stick! 28
Circle time 29
Role play! 30
Sing and move! 31
Listen and do! 32
Rhyme time! 33
Write-in activities 34-36
Numbers 1-10
Listen, point and say! 37
Sing and point! 38
Musical instruments
Listen and point! 39
Listen and stick! 40
Sing and move! 41
Drum or clap! 42
Rhyme time! 43
Write-in activities 44-46
Review 47

Part 3 Sound Discrimination - Body percussion
My feelings 48
Listen and point! 49
Listen, stick and think! 50
Story time 51
Sing and move! 52
Mirror time / Rhyme time 53
Write-in activities 54-57
My body
Listen and point! 58
Stick and build! 59
Game. **My face** - Listen and point! 60
Rhyme time! 61
Sing and move! 62
Mirror time / Circle time 63
Write-in activities 64-65
Review 66

Part 4 Rhythm and rhyme
Colours
Listen and speak! 67
Listen and point! 68
Listen and stick! 69
Game - Traffic lights 70
Sing and move! 71
Drum or clap! 72
Rhyme time! 73
Write-in activities 74-77
Shapes
Listen and point! 78
Listen and stick! 79
Game / Rhyme time 80
Sing and move! 81
Drum or clap! 82
Write-in activities 83-86
Review 87

Good bye Chant / Song 88

Teachers, supervisors and parents
At the bottom of each page you will find **teaching notes**. These notes provide explanation and information about the activities on each page so you are aware of the objectives.

Arrows → Instructions on how to complete an activity.

Lesson Structure
1. Start every Letterland lesson with the '**Hello**' song.
(See *Fix-it Phonics Starter Audio CD - Track 1* or Software)
2. Review previous learning with role play and/or circle time,
3. Introduce a new topic/letter sound and action. Complete as much as time allows.
4. End each lesson with the '**Good bye**' chant and song.
(See *Fix-it Phonics Starter Audio CD 1 - Track 59* or Software)

Sing → Listen to the song first. Then join in with just the '**hello**' and '**hi**'. Finally sing the whole song together!

Sing and move!

Hi, hello! Let's wave! Hello.

Hi, hello! Let's wave! Hello.

How are you?

I'm fine, thank you!

Hello, hello. Ok, let's go!

Let's go to Letterland! (x2)

Sing this song at the start of every Letterland session/lesson to reinforce how to say '**hello**' in a memorable, fun and inclusive way.

Listen!

Listen to these Letterland friends saying '**hi**'. The second time you hear it, join in by saying '**hi**' or '**hello**' back.

Listen and speak!

Hi! Hello!

Listening to different voices allows children to gain awareness of different accents, male and female voices, pitch and volume.

Hello! Sit in a circle. Choose a child to start. They say '**hello!**'. Clockwise each child must follow. Get faster and faster around the circle.

Circle time - Hello!

Week 1	Hello. Hi.	**Part 2**	Hello. Hi. My name is...
Part 3	Hello. Hi. My name is... I am ____(age)	**Part 4**	Hello. Hi. My name is... I am ___ (age). I like (colour).

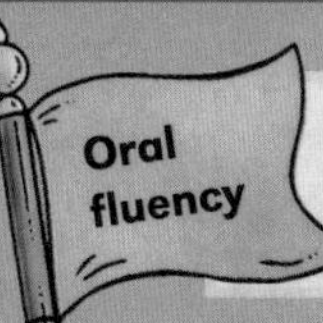

A vital part of language learning is being able to use it with fluency and expression. Use circle time to build confidence in making sounds.

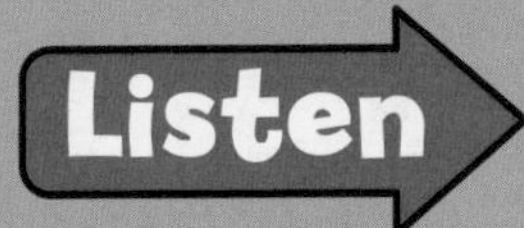

Who's at the door? Listen to this Letterland friend saying '**hello**' and his name. Then you try to say hello back!

Hi.
My name is
Harry Hat
Man.

Talk

With a friend, pretend to knock at a door. When your friend opens the door say '**Hello**', and say your name. Take turns.

Role play - Who is at the door?

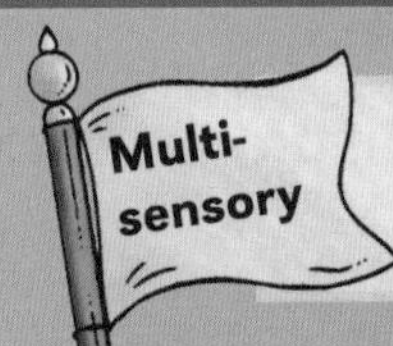

Linking movements and actions with words makes learning really motivating and memorable.

Animal noises Let's get our ears ready for learning.
Listen and point to the the animal you hear.

Listen and point!

Act In pairs, take turns to make animal noises. You can also do actions. The other person must guess or point to the correct picture above.

Play in pairs!

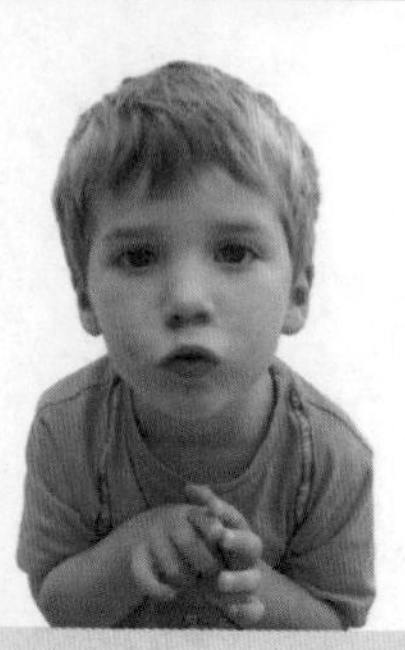

Working with a partner ensures that ***all*** children are involved in an activity. Participation brings confidence in speaking skills.

Stickers!

Listen and stick. Listen to the sounds of these animals and put your stickers in the correct order.

Listen and stick!

1 2 3

4 5 6

Recognition of sounds in sequence really improves listening skills. Then use your software to play the 'Animal noises' game.

Listen to the song first, then join in with just the animal sounds and make up actions. Finally sing the whole song together.

Software includes animated songs!

Sing and move!

Hello, rat. Eee, eee, eee!

Hello, cat. Miaow! Miaow!

Hello, dog. Woof, woof, woof!

Ooooooo! Let's run! (x2)

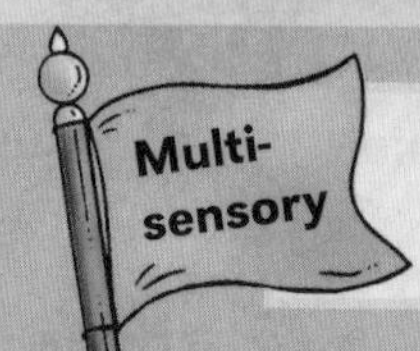

Having fun making sounds and linking movement with learning new words makes it more motivating and memorable.

Listen to the words. Then listen as the drum plays for each syllable in the word. You try clapping or drumming the syllables.

Drum or clap!

dog

●

cat

●

rat

●

tiger

● ●

monkey

● ●

zebra

● ●

Being able to identify syllables allows children to begin to associate spoken language with written words.

Noisy farm! In a circle, child 1 repeats an animal sound, e.g. '**moo, moo...**'. Each child joins in with new sounds until it's a noisy farmyard!

Circle time - Animals!

Oral fluency

A vital part of language learning is being able to use it with fluency and expression. Use circle time to build confidence in making sounds.

Rhyme

Listen to the rhyme and identify the words that rhyme. Listen to the rhyme again but this time, you say the rhyming words!

Rhyme time!

The cat sat on the mat.

The cat sat on the mat.

Hello, rat!

Bye bye, cat and rat!

Hearing and identifying rhyming words helps children to become phonologically aware. This is an important first step in reading.

Circle the one that is different.

What comes next in this sequence?

Draw it in the last box.

Draw a ring around the animal that rhymes with **mat**.

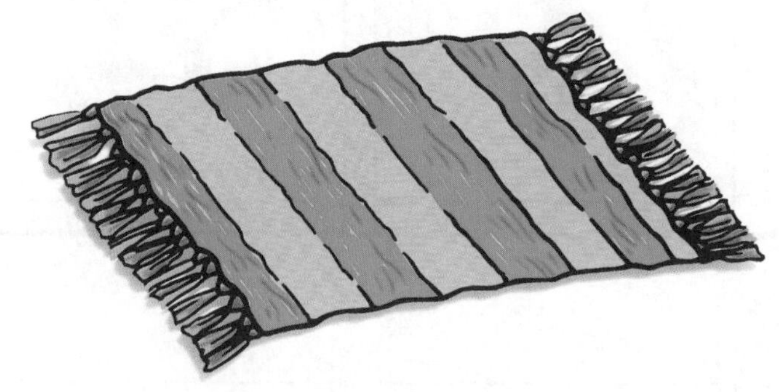

Now draw a **rat**  on a **mat**. 

Colour the **loudest** animal.

Outdoor noises

Let's get our ears ready for learning!
Listen and point to the things you hear.

Listen and point!

Act

In pairs, take turns to make outdoor noises. You can also do actions. The other person must guess or point to the correct picture above.

Play in pairs!

Working with a partner ensures that **all** children are involved in an activity. Participation brings confidence in speaking skills.

Stickers!

Listen and stick. Listen to these outdoor noises and put your stickers in the correct order.

Listen and stick!

Recognition of sounds in sequence really improves listening skills. Use your software to play the 'Outdoor noises' game.

Listen to the song first, then join in with actions. Make a train with children joining together. '**Moo**' like a cow, then STOP!

Software includes animated songs!

Sing and move!

Chugga, chugga, chugga, chugga,

goes the train.

Chugga, chugga, chugga, chugga.

Chugga, chugga, chugga, chugga.

Choo, choo!

Moo, moo! STOP! Phew! (x2)

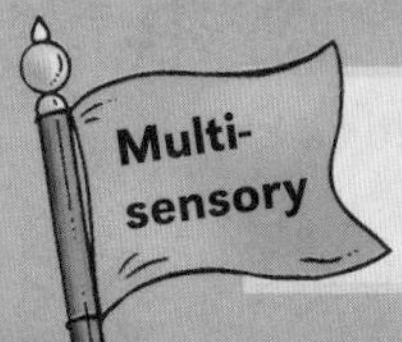

Having fun making sounds and linking movement with learning builds confidence in communication skills.

Listen to the words. Then listen as the drum plays for each syllable in the word. You try clapping or drumming the syllables.

Drum or clap!

car

●

train

●

bike

●

tractor

● ●

scooter

● ●

helicopter

● ● ● ●

Being able to identify syllables allows children to begin to associate spoken language with written words.

Traffic jam! In a circle, children make a '**brum, brum**' or '**beep, beep**' noise. Clockwise each child joins in until you have a very noisy traffic jam!

Circle time - Traffic jam!

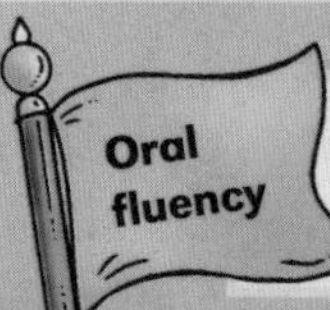

A vital part of language learning is being able to use it with fluency and expression. Use circle time to build confidence in making sounds.

Rhyme

Listen to the rhyme and identify the words that rhyme. Listen to the rhyme again but this time, you say the rhyming words!

Rhyme time!

I can fly,
up in the sky.

Look at me,
down in the sea!

fly

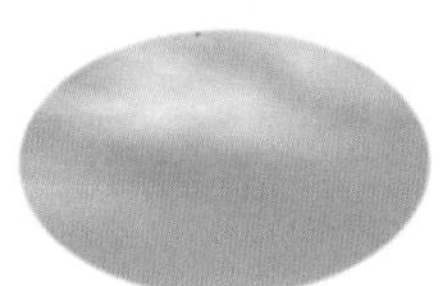

sky

me

sea

Hearing and identifying rhyming words helps children to become phonologically aware. This is an important first step in reading.

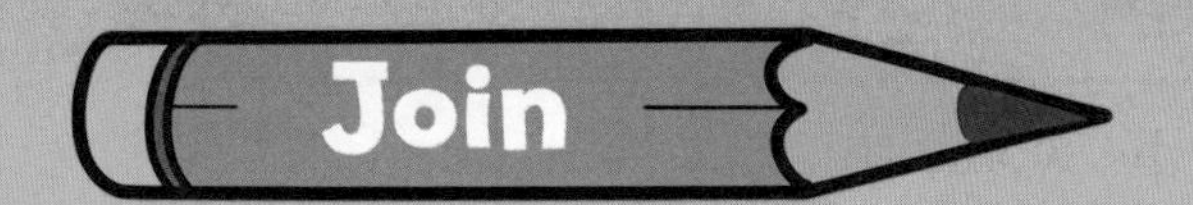

Join these pictures to the word that rhymes with **fly**.

fly in the

fly in the

fly in the

Find five differences between these two pictures. Circle them.

Answer: goat changed direction; plane moved; helicopter appeared; fire engine has lights on; cow appeared.

Follow the tracks to the tractor with your pencil.

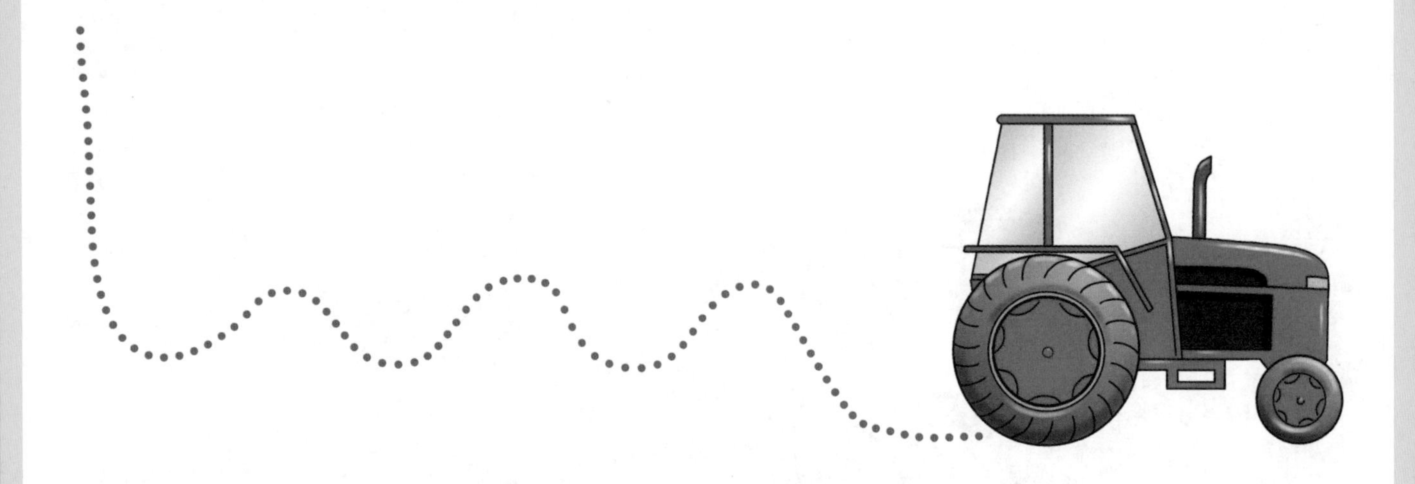

Now guide the tractor along the tracks to the farm house.

Find five things in this picture that make lots of noise!

Answer: helicopter; plane; fire engine; train; truck.

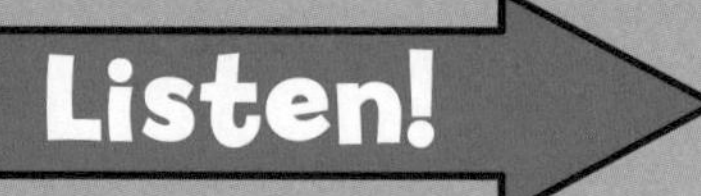

Let's say hello, your name and how old you are.
Listen to Fix-it Max first, then you try.

Listen and speak!

Hello. I'm Fix-it Max. I'm six.

Listening to different voices allows children to gain awareness of different accents, male and female voices, pitch and volume.

Numbers! Listen and point to the number you hear.

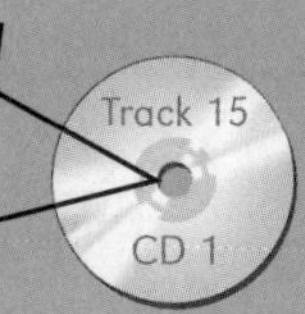

Listen and point!

1 2 3

4 5 6

Drum

In pairs, take turns to bang a drum / tap the table. The other person must listen and count the beats then point to the correct number above.

Play in pairs!

Pair work

Working with a partner ensures that ***all*** children are involved in an activity. Participation brings confidence in speaking skills.

Stickers!

Listen and stick. Listen and count the beats.
Put your stickers in the correct order.

Listen and stick!

Sequence

Recognition of words in sequence improves listening and number skills. Use your software to play another listening game.

Numbers! Sit in a circle. A child/teacher says the number 1. Pass it around the circle. When it has been around the whole circle, move on to number 2, and so on until you reach number 6.

Circle time - Numbers!

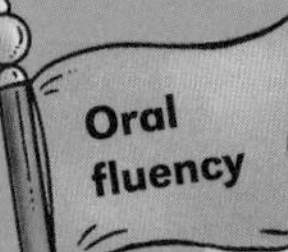

Use circle time to build confidence in making sounds. Vary the speed and complexity of sounds depending on the children's abilities.

Listen to these Letterland friends playing a game. Guess how many balls are in the cup. You try playing the game with a friend.

Talk

You will need: a cup, pebbles/small counters. One person covers their eyes, while the other puts counters under the cup. Guess how many!

Role play - How many?

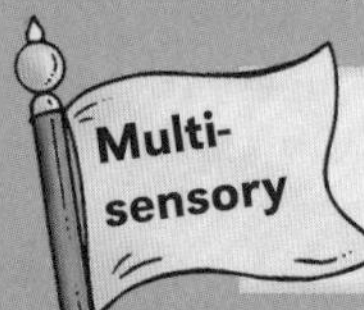

Linking games with words makes learning really motivating and memorable.

Sing

Listen to the song first, then join in with actions such as counting on fingers and clapping. Finally sing the whole song together.

Software includes animated songs!

Sing and move!

1, 2, 3. (Clap, clap clap!)

4, 5, 6. (Clap, clap clap!)

1, 2, 3, 4, 5, 6.

(Clap, clap, clap, clap, clap, clap!)

1, 2, 3, 4, 5, 6. (x2)

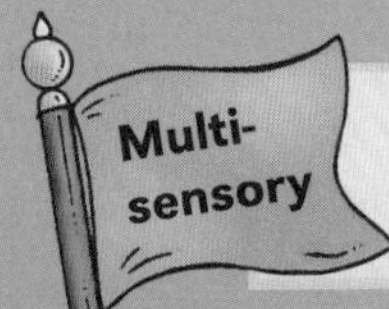

Having fun making sounds and linking movement with learning new words makes it more motivating and memorable.

Listen Just listen to the instructions the first time. The second time, listen and join in with the instructions.

Listen and do!

Clap 4 times.

Stand up.

Wave 3 times.

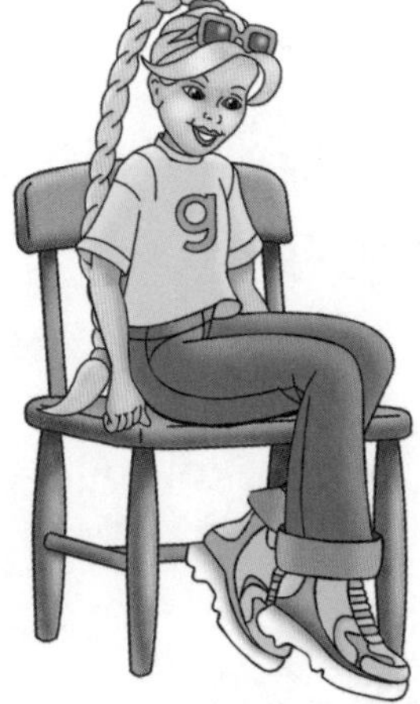

Sit down.

Open your book.

Close your book.

Multi-sensory Linking movement with learning this new, useful classroom language makes it more motivating and memorable.

Rhyme

Listen to the rhyme and identify the words that rhyme. Listen to the rhyme again but this time, you say the rhyming words!

Rhyme time!

One, two, three.

Count with me.

Four, five, six.

Six big sticks!

3		6	
three	me	six	sticks

Hearing and identifying rhyming words helps children to become phonologically aware. This is an important first step in reading.

How old are you? Draw the correct number of candles on the cake. Then colour it in.

Count the animals and join them to the correct number.

What comes next in the sequence? Write the number and finish the picture.

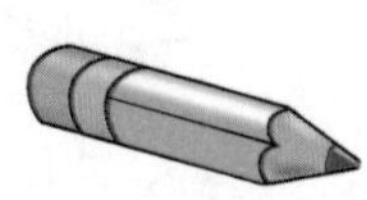

Listen Listen and revise number 1-6. Then listen, point and say the numbers 7-10.

Listen, point and say!

1 2 3 4 5 6 7 8 9 10

Try finding and counting things you see in the classroom.
Count how many pencils or friends you have.

Sing

Listen to the song first, then join in with the counting actions.
Finally sing the whole song together.

Software includes animated songs!

Sing and point!

1, 2, 3. Count with me.

4, 5. High five!

6, 7, 8. That's great!

9, 10. Let's start again.

1, 2, 3. Count with me.

4, 5. High five!

6, 7, 8. That's great!

9, 10. Let's stop!

Multi-sensory

Children develop their communication skills and expand their vocabulary by listening and singing along to songs.

Music! Listen and point to the instrument you hear.

Listen and point!

Act

In pairs, take turns to play or pretend to play musical instruments. The other person must guess or point to the correct picture above.

Play in pairs!

Pair work

Working with a partner ensures that ***all*** children are involved in an activity. Participation brings confidence in speaking skills.

Stickers!

Listen and stick. Listen to the instruments.
Put your stickers in the correct order.

Listen and stick!

1 2 3

4 5 6

Sequence

Recognition of sounds in sequence really improves listening skills.
Use your software to play another music listening game.

Sing Listen to the song first, then join in with just the actions.
Finally sing the whole song together.

Software includes animated songs!

Sing and move!

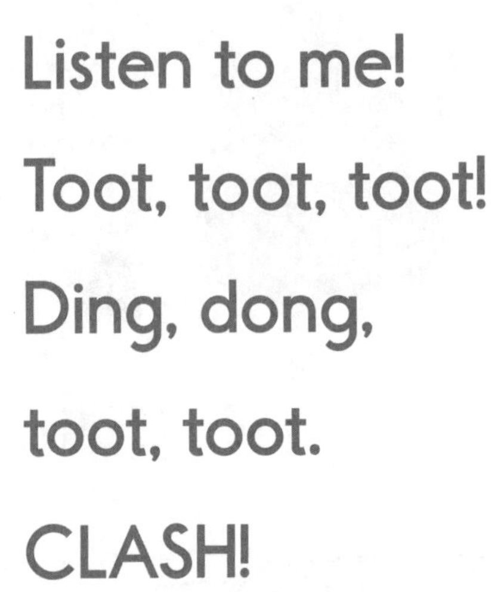

Listen to me!
Toot, toot, toot!
Listen to me!
Drum, drum, drum.
Listen to me!
Toot, toot, toot!
Ding, dong,
toot, toot.
CLASH!

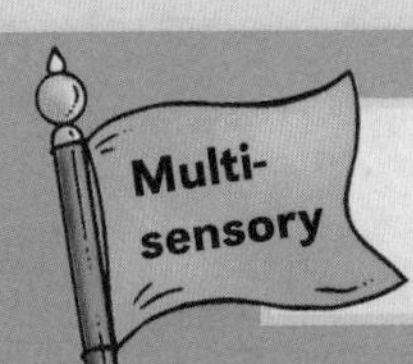

Having fun making sounds and linking movement with learning new words makes it more motivating and memorable.

Clap Each with an instrument or just clapping / tapping the desk, listen to the instructions and then join in.

Drum or clap!

fast

slow

quiet 

loud

fast and loud

slow and quiet

Loud Quiet In a circle, children pass an instrument. As it is passed the instructions such as '**fast**', '**slow**', '**quiet**' and '**loud**' can be given.

Circle time - Music!

Encouraging children to listen attentively is very important.
A good listener becomes a good language learner.

Rhyme

Listen to the rhyme. The aim is to identify the words that rhyme - not to understand every word.

Rhyme time!

Ben has a bell.

He hangs it on a tree.

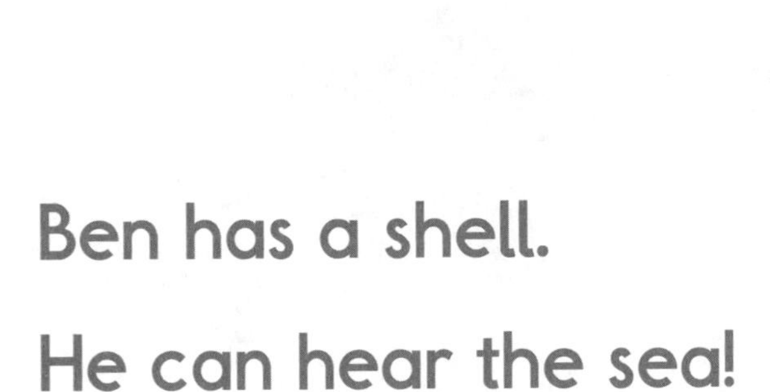

Ben has a shell.

He can hear the sea!

bell	shell	tree	sea

Hearing and identifying rhyming words helps children to become phonologically aware. This is an important first step in reading.

Join the dots to finish the drum, then colour it in.

Find five differences between these two pictures. Circle them.

Answer: maracas changed colour; Red Robot appeared; poster with drum appeared; Dippy Duck has a bell; it is night time.

Which two of these drums are exactly the **same**? Join them.

Let's see how much you can remember! Put a tick next to the word you hear. The first one has been done for you.

Let's check!

1. 3  

2.   

3.    

4.   

5. 

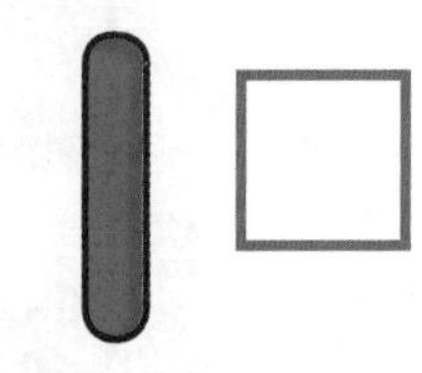

6.     

Decide whether you think your class is ready for this assessment. If it would be too challenging for individuals, simply move on or complete it as a group activity.

Listen!

Listen to Harry Hat Man saying his name and how he feels. Then you try repeating it!

Listen and speak!

I feel happy!

Listen

Listen to these Letterland friends saying how they feel.
Then you try, '**How do you feel?**' '**I feel... '**

Making different voices is fun and encourages good listening skills.
Try talking just like Harry Hat Man.

Listen and stick! - Animal noises

Page 7

Listen and stick! - Outdoor noises

Page 17

Listen and stick! - Drum beats

Page 28

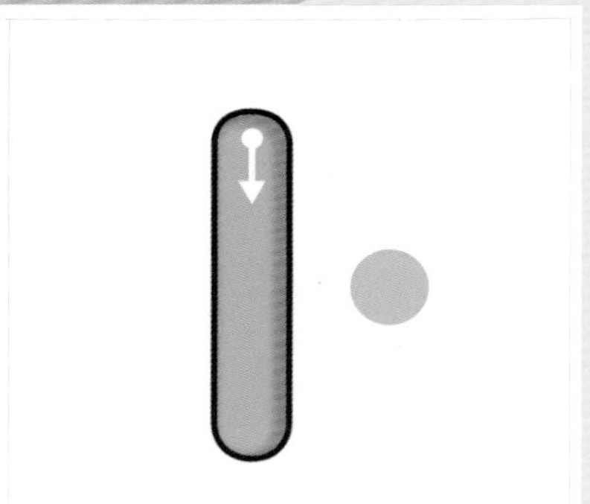

Listen and stick! - Music

Page 40

Listen and stick! - Feelings

Page 50

Stick and build! - The body

Page 59

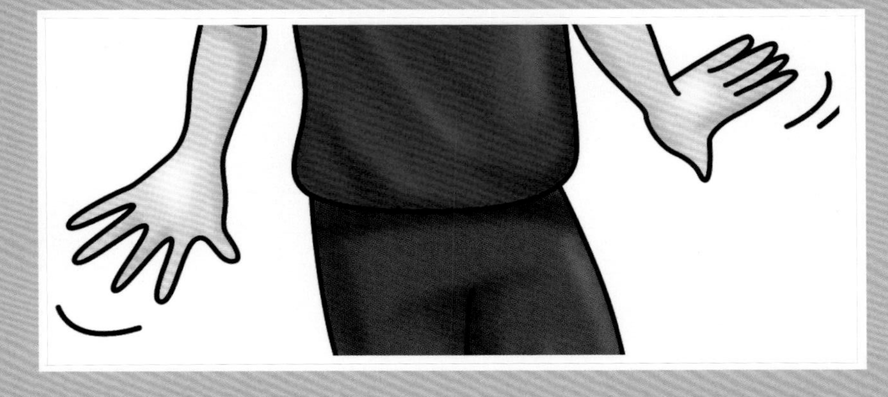

Great work!

Listen and stick! - Colours

Page 69

Listen and stick! - Shapes

Page 79

Reward stars

Listen and point!

Act

In pairs, take turns to make faces of the different feelings above.
The other person must guess the feeling.

Play in pairs!

Working with a partner ensures that ***all*** children are involved in an activity. Participation brings confidence in speaking skills.

Stickers!

Listen and stick. Listen and put your stickers in the correct order.

Listen and stick!

Think!

How do you feel now? Choose a sticker to show your mood.

How do you feel? I feel...

Talk

With friends, take turns to ask, '**How do you feel?**' answering with a facial expression as well as the words.

Giving time to to think and relate words to situations helps internalise learning. Play the 'Feelings' game on your software.

Sammy's story

Look at the pictures and talk about what is happening. How does Sammy feel in each picture? Then listen to the story.

Linking words to a sequence of events is the first stage in story-telling.

Song

Listen to the song first, then join in with just the actions.
Finally sing the whole song together.

Software includes animated songs!

Sing and move!

I am happy, happy, happy,
so I'll laugh.

I am angry, angry, angry,
so I'll stomp!

I am sad, sad, sad,
so I'll cry.

I am scared, scared, scared,
so I'll scream! (x2)

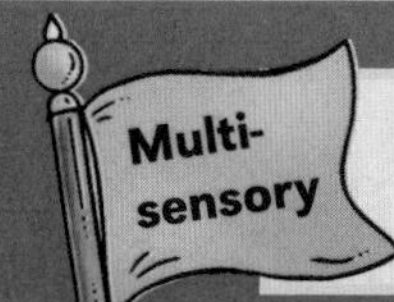

Children develop their communication skills by singing along to songs. The aim is to have fun and have a basic understanding, not to teach every word.

Look

Use a mirror and look at your face in the mirror.
Make different faces - sad, happy, angry, scared and sleepy.

Mirror time!

Look at your face!

Teacher preparation Providing a small mirror each, allows children to really look at their face and mouth position when forming sounds and words.

Rhyme

Listen to the rhyme. The aim is to identify the words that rhyme - not to understand every word.

Track 35 CD 1

Rhyme time!

Look at me.

I am happy!

Look at Dad.

He is sad.

me happy dad sad

Hearing and identifying rhyming words helps children to become phonologically aware. This is an important first step in reading.

Complete the faces to match the words.

Join the happy faces to Harry Hat Man.

Join the sad faces to Sammy Snake.

Who is scared in this picture? Circle them.

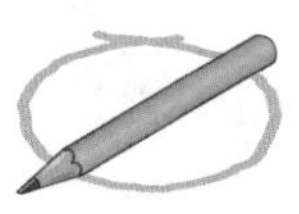

What makes you scared? Draw it here.

Which two of these faces are exactly the **same**? Join them.

The body! Listen and point to the body.

Listen and point!

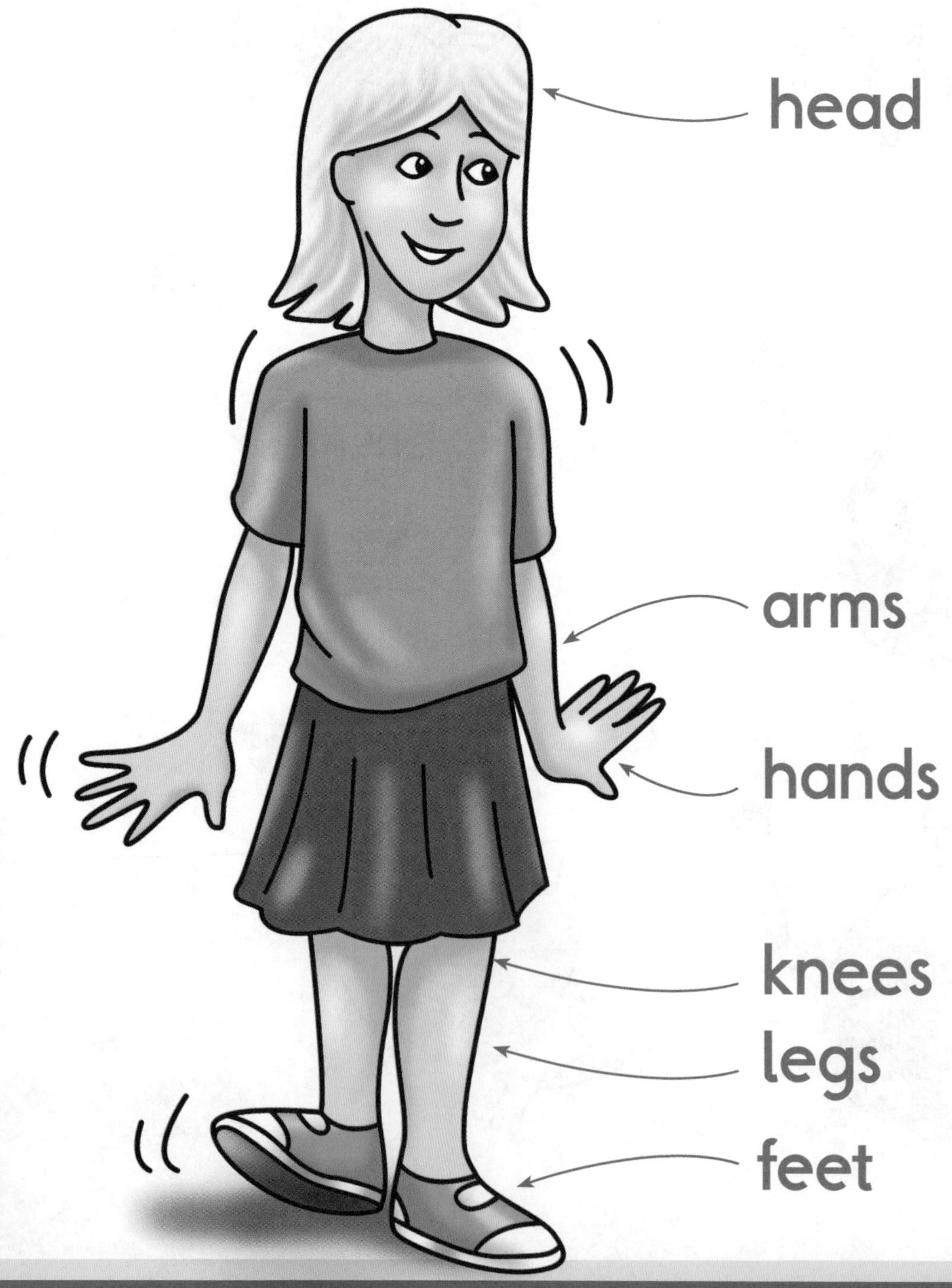

This exercise improves listening and comprehension skills so children can start to identify words quickly.

Stickers!

Look at your stickers and see if you can build a body starting at the feet. As you build the body, name the parts you know.

Stick and build!

Thinking skills

Taking the time to think about the words and saying them as the body is built allows children to consolidate the new vocabulary.

Game

Listen first, then take turns to stand at the front of the group and give instructions for others to follow. e.g. '**Hands on heads, hands**...'.

Lead the group!

Use this activity to build confidence. Choose only those children who *want* to lead the class.

Listen to the new words to describe the face. The first time just listen. The second time, point and say the words.

My face - Listen and point!

This exercise improves listening and comprehension skills so children can start to identify words quickly.

Rhyme

Listen to the rhyme. The aim is to identify the words that rhyme - not to understand every word.

Rhyme time!

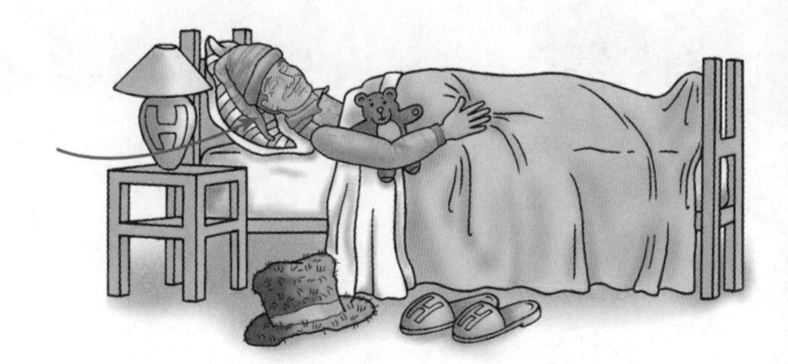

His head is on the bed.

Her hand is in the sand.

His knee is in the tree.

head	hand	knee
bed	sand	tree

Hearing and identifying rhyming words helps children to become phonologically aware. This is an important first step in reading.

Sing Listen to the song first, then join in with some actions. Finally sing the whole song together.

Software includes animated songs!

Sing and move!

Put your hands on your head
and jump!

Put your hands on your mouth
and jump!

Put your hands on your legs
and turn around.

Stamp your feet and
then sit down!

Multi-sensory Children develop their communication skills by listening and singing along to songs.

Mouth

Listen to the sounds. Then try forming them. Look into a mirror as you make the sounds to become aware of the mouth positions.

Teacher preparation Providing a small mirror each, allows children to really look at their face and mouth position when forming sounds and words.

Mirror time!

a e i o u

Vowel names In a circle, children pass a vowel name around. It should go around the full circle before the next is introduced.

Circle time - sound chain

Make really pronounced mouth movements so children become aware of how their mouths form sounds. This helps with the articulation of words.

1. You will need a friend to play.
Get a piece of paper.
Draw a **head**.
Fold it over.
Pass it on.

2. Draw a **body** and **arms**.
Fold it over. Pass it on.

3. Draw **legs**.
Fold it over. Pass it on.

4. Draw **feet**. Fold over, pass on.

Open it up to see the funny creature you have made!

Draw a funny monster body with:

1 nose **2** mouths **3** legs **4** arms **5** hands **6** eyes

Review

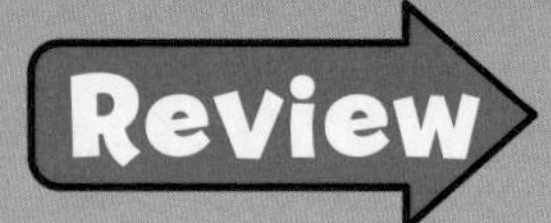

Let's see how much you can remember! Listen and put a tick next to the matching picture. The first one has been done for you.

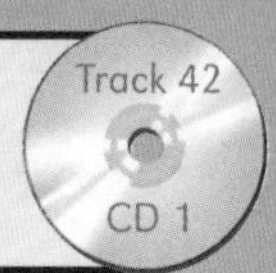

Track 42
CD 1

Let's check!

1. 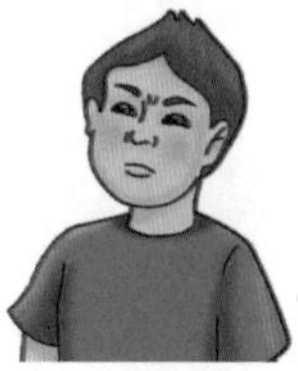 ☑ 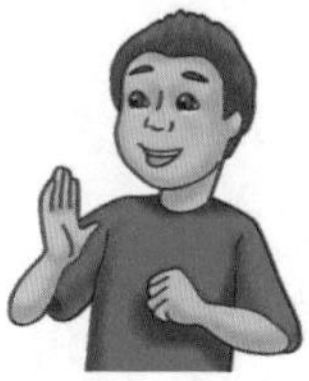 ☐ 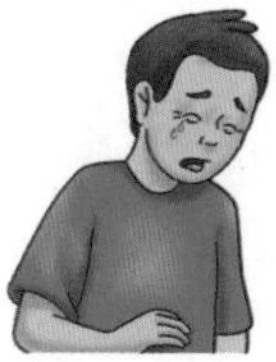 ☐

2. 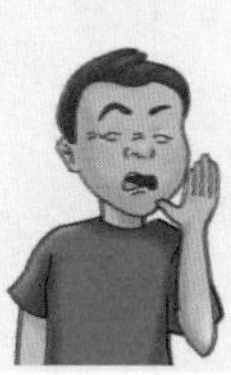 ☐ 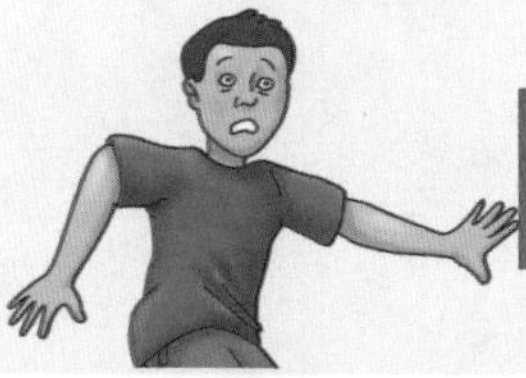 ☐ 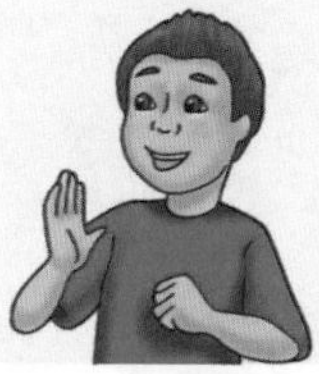 ☐

3. 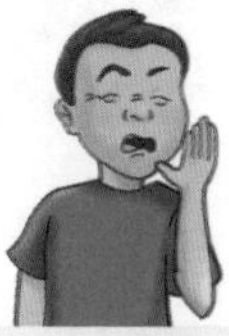 ☐ 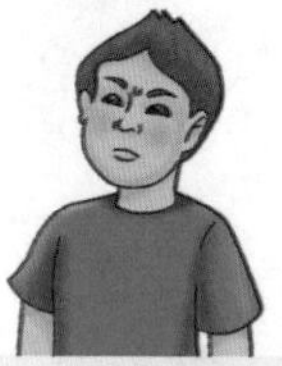 ☐ 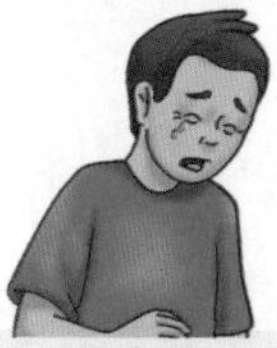 ☐

4. 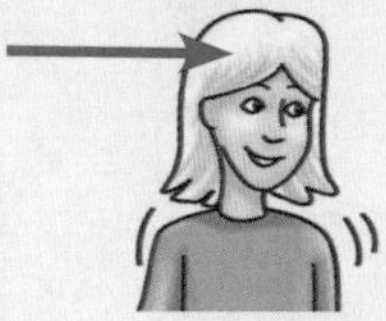 ☐ 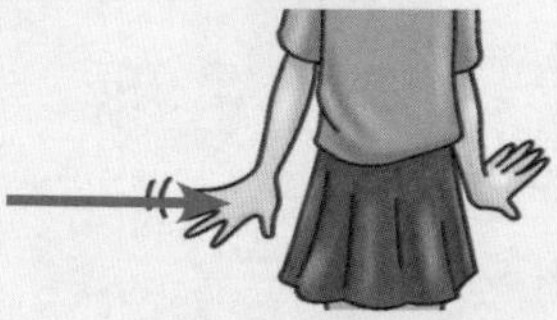 ☐ 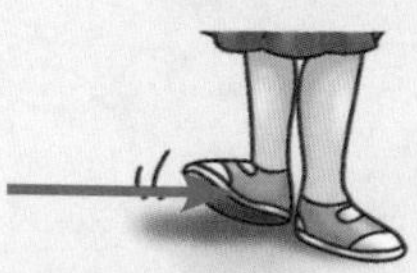 ☐

5. 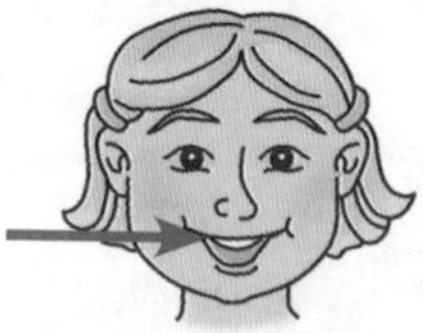 ☐ 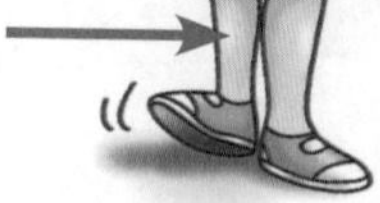 ☐ 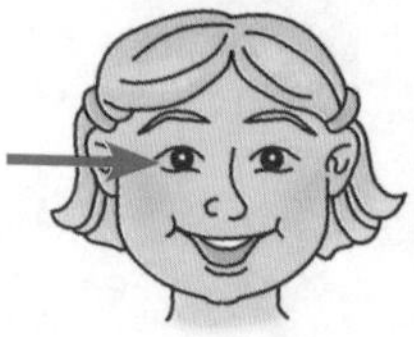 ☐

6. 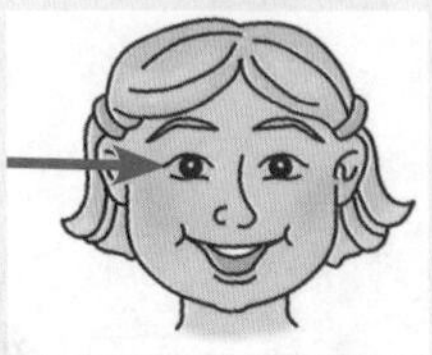 ☐ 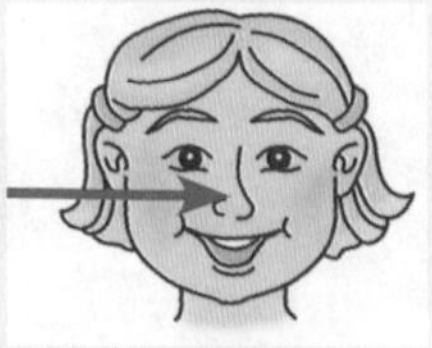 ☐ 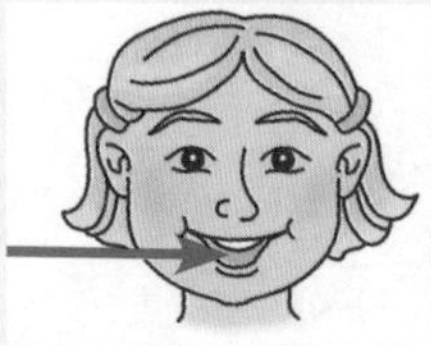 ☐

Review

Decide whether you think your class is ready for this assessment. If it would be too challenging for individuals, simply move on or complete it as a group activity.

Listen!

Listen to Red Robot saying his name and the colour he likes the most. Then you try repeating it in a robot voice!

Listen and speak!

Hello.
I'm Red Robot.
I like red!

I like red.

Making different voices is fun and encourages good listening skills. Try talking just like Red Robot.

Colours! Listen and point to the colour.

Listen and point!

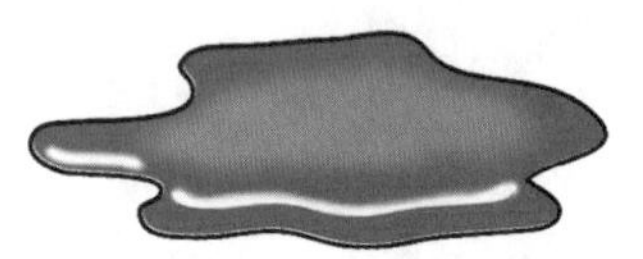
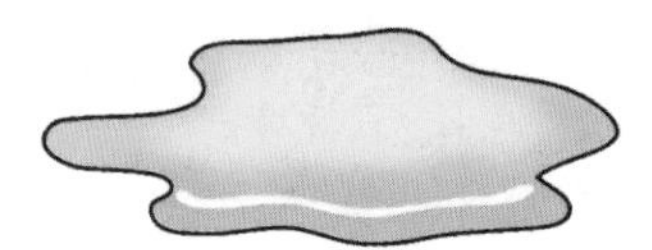
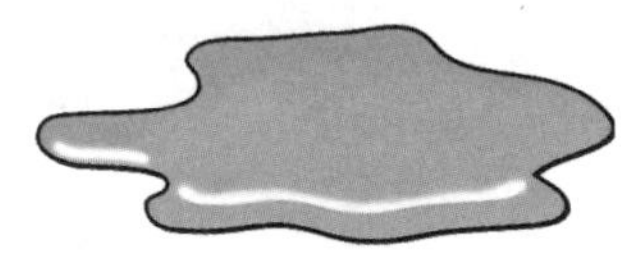

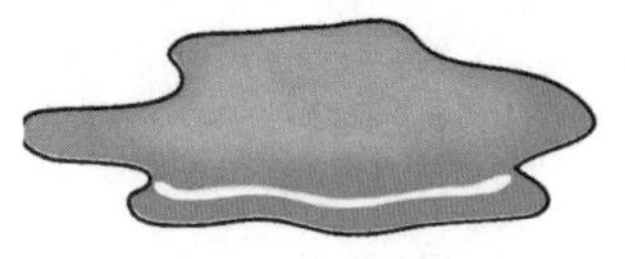
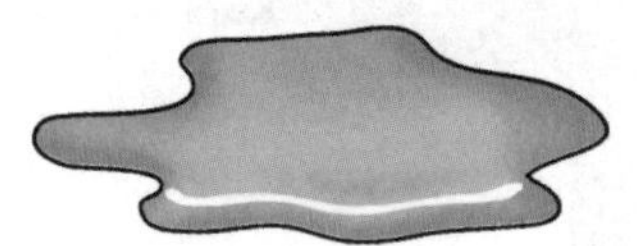
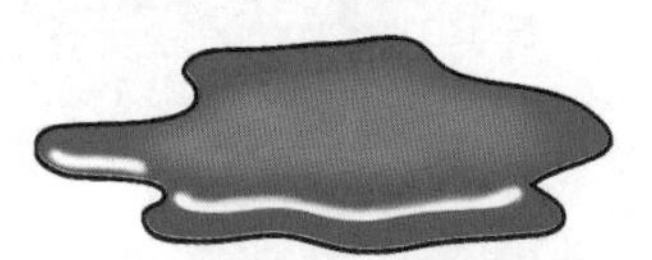

Act In pairs, take turns to point to the colours above. The other person must say the colour as quickly as possible.

Play in pairs!

Working with a partner ensures that **all** children are involved in an activity. Participation brings confidence in speaking skills.

Stickers!

Listen and stick. Listen to the colours. Put the correct stickers in the boxes in order.

Listen and stick!

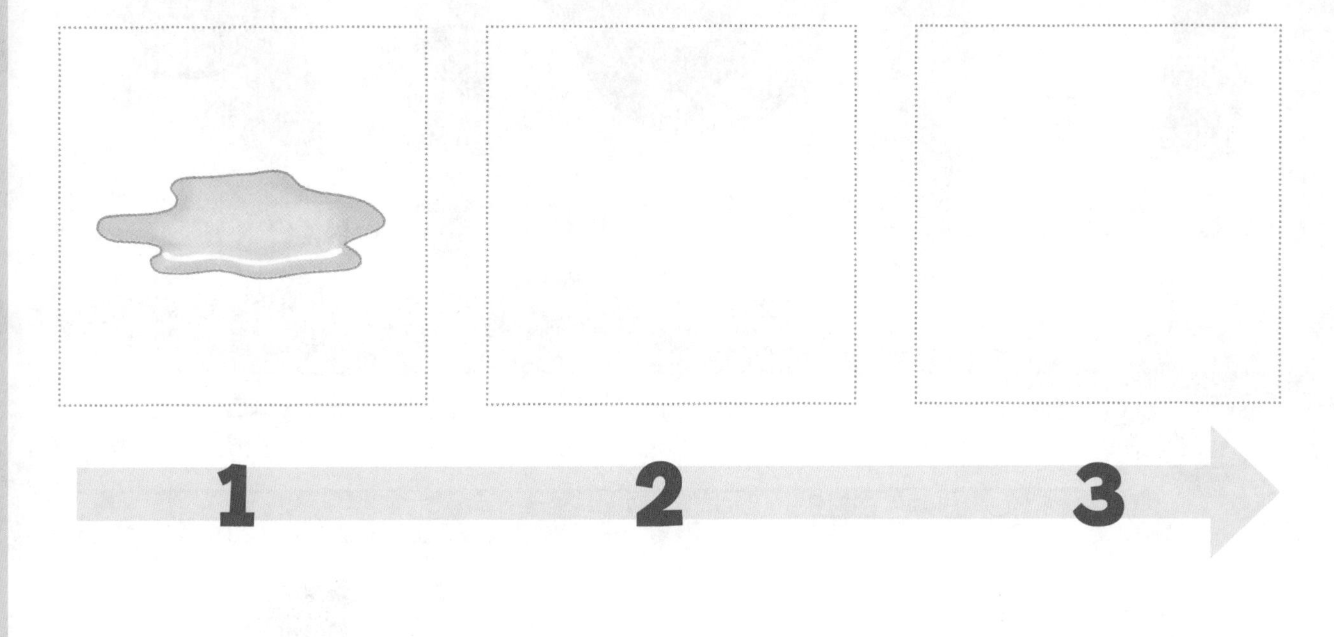

1 2 3

4 5 6

Recognition of words in sequence really improves listening skills.

Listen Listen to these Letterland friends saying the colours they like the most. Then you try, '**I like...**'.

I like red.

I like orange.

I like green.

Game A child/teacher is the traffic light. When they shout out '**red**' - stop moving, '**orange**' - get ready position, '**green**' - walk around the room.

Multi-sensory Linking movement with learning these colours makes it more motivating and memorable.

Song

Listen to the song first, then join in with just the actions. Finally sing the whole song together.

Software includes animated songs!

Sing and move!

Rainbow, rainbow.

Red and yellow.

Rainbow, rainbow.

Green and blue.

Red and yellow and green and blue!

Rainbow, rainbow. I like you! (x2)

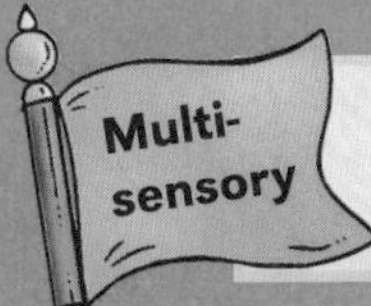

Children develop their communication skills by listening and singing along to songs.

Listen to the words. Then listen as the drum plays for each syllable in the word. You try clapping or drumming the syllables.

Drum or clap!

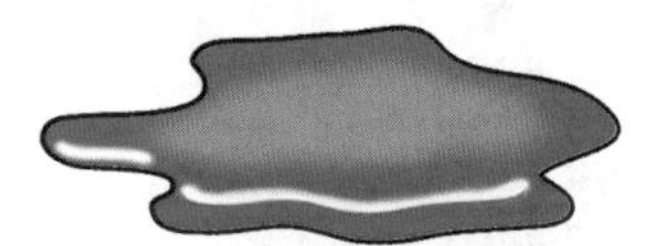

red

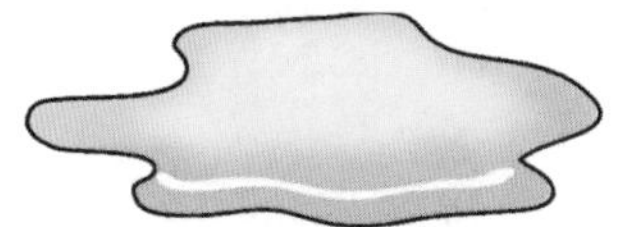

yellow

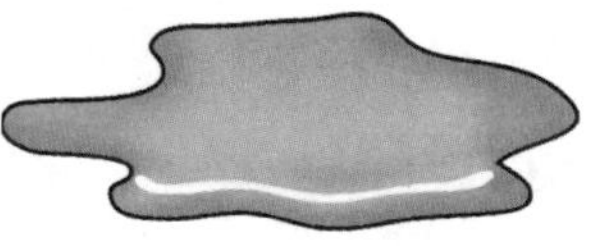

blue

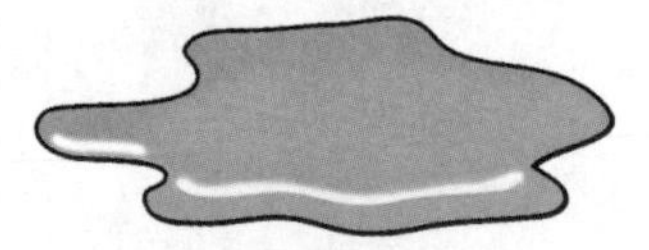

green

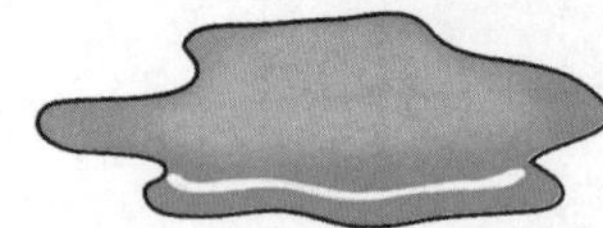

orange

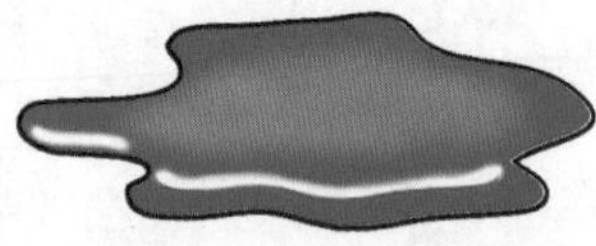

pink

Syllable clapping

Being able to identify syllables allows children to begin to associate spoken language with written words.

Rhyme

Listen to the rhyme. The aim is to identify the words that rhyme - not to understand every word.

Rhyme time!

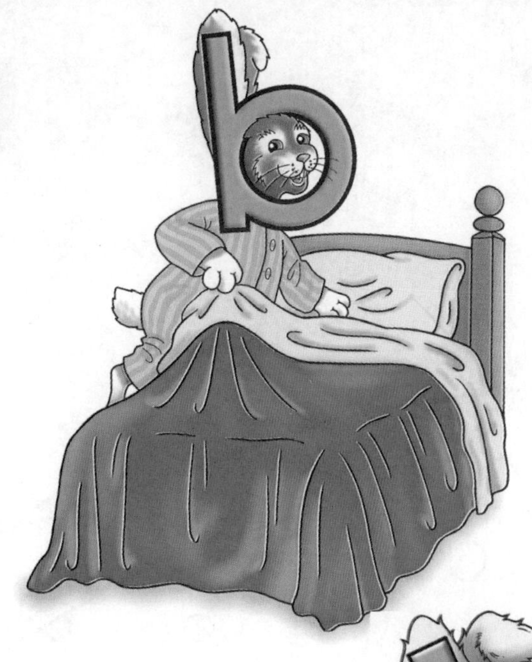

Red, red.

I like my red bed!

Blue, blue.

Where is my blue shoe?

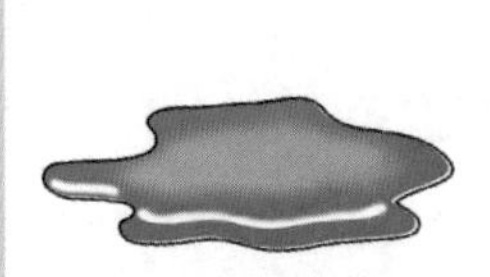

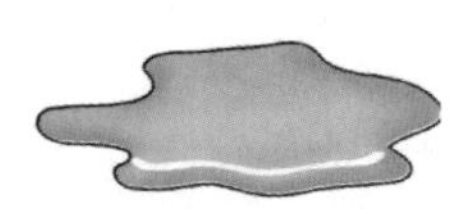

red bed blue shoe

Hearing and identifying rhyming words helps children to become phonologically aware. This is an important first step in reading.

Colour by numbers!

1 2 3 4 5 6

Use the repeating patterns to finish colouring this picture.

Trace the patterns and colour in the picture.

Can you find six differences between these two pictures?

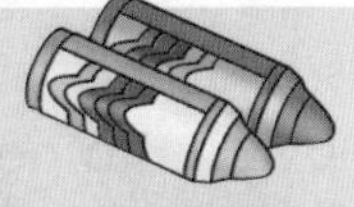

Answer: rainbow stripe changed colour; helicopter changed colour; cow changed colour; car changed colour; hat on horse changed colour; centre of flower changed colo

Shapes! Listen and point to the shapes.

Listen and point!

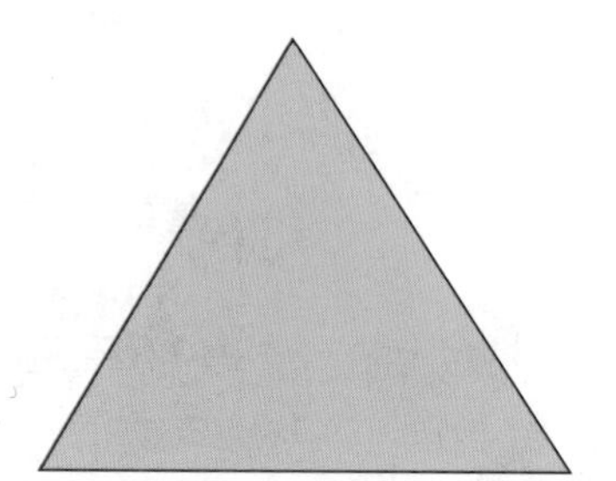

Listen Listen and point to the correct shape as fast as you can.
Listen carefully as it gets faster and faster!

Listen again!

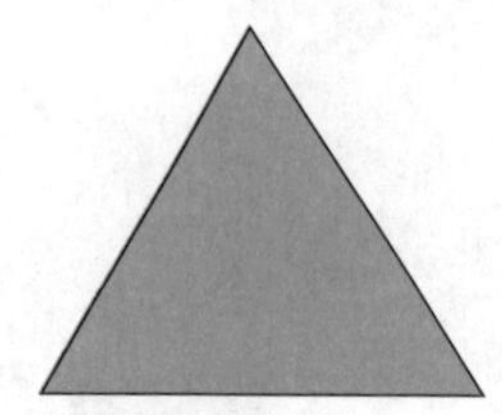

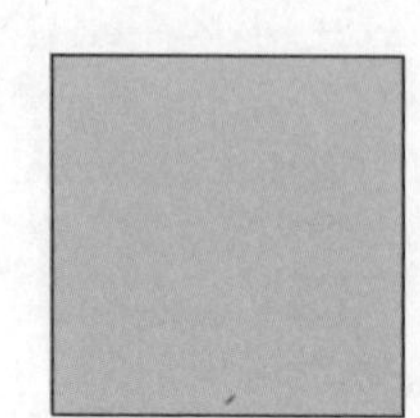

Children learn at different rates. This exercise combines knowledge of colours and shapes. If your class is not ready for this, simply move on to page 81. The learning of colours and shapes is consolidated in *Fix-it Phonics - Level 1*.

Stickers!

Listen and stick. Ben likes to build towers. Listen and put your stickers in the correct order to build the tower.

Listen and stick!

Recognition of words in sequence really improves listening skills.

Game

Musical Shapes! As the music plays, dance about.
When the music stops, listen and go to the correct shape.

Teacher Preparation Cut out four shapes: red circle, green square, yellow rectangle, blue triangle. Put them on the floor/on the wall in the corners of the room.

Rhyme

Listen to the rhyme. The aim is to identify the words that rhyme - not to understand every word.

Rhyme time!

Where, oh, where
is the green square?

The green square is
on the green chair!

where

chair

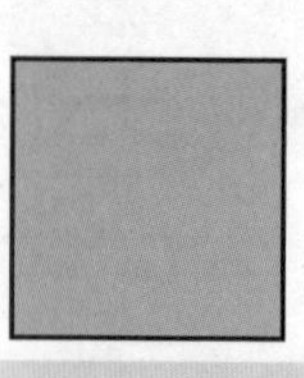

square

Hearing and identifying rhyming words helps children to become phonologically aware. This is an important first step in reading.

Song

Listen to the song first, then join in with just the actions.
Finally sing the whole song together.

Software includes animated songs!

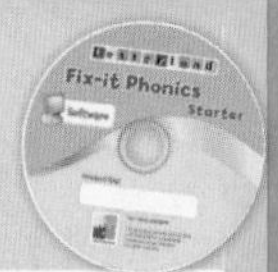

Sing and move!

Draw a triangle on a circle.
Draw a rectangle on a square.
Circle, triangle, rectangle, square.
Draw them all, then sit on a chair. (x2)

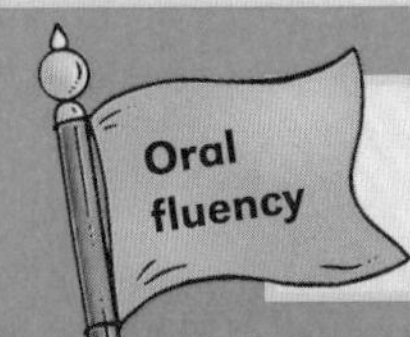

Children develop their communication skills by listening and singing along to songs.

Listen to the words. Then listen as the drum plays for each syllable in the word. You try clapping or drumming the syllables.

Drum or clap!

square

circle

rectangle

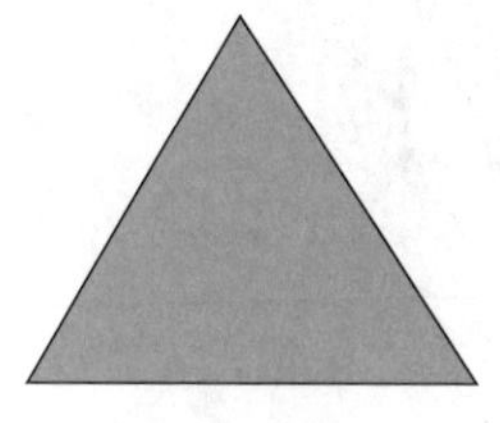

triangle

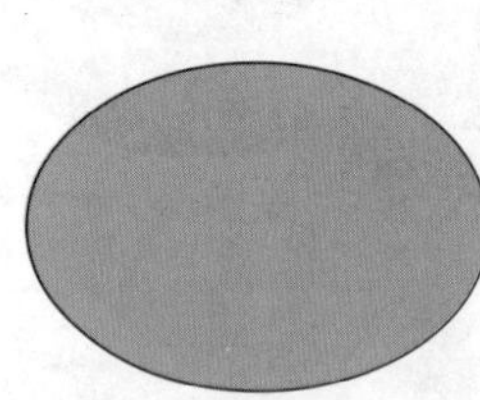

oval

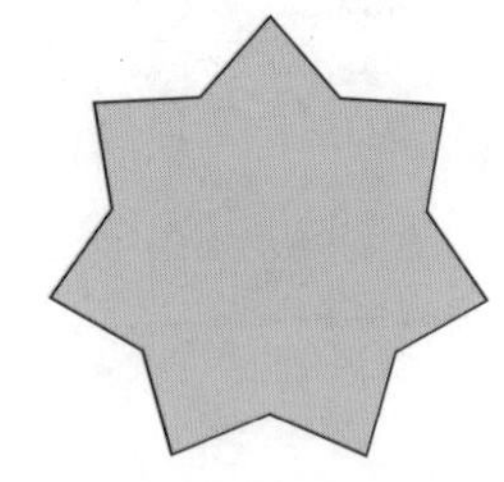

star

Syllable clapping

Being able to identify syllables allows children to begin to associate spoken language with written words.

Find and colour these shapes!

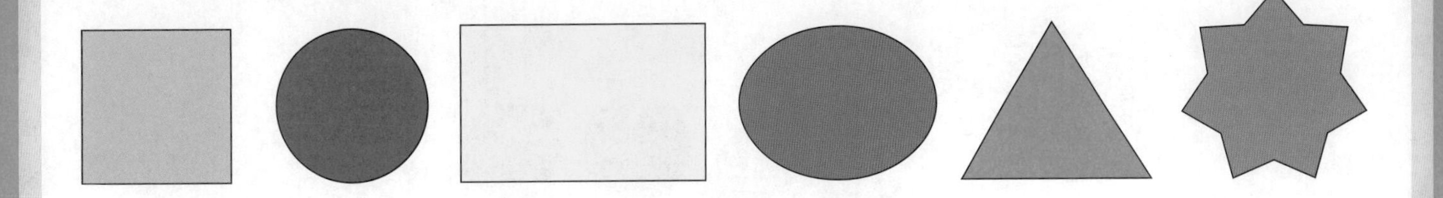

Follow the repeating pattern to create a beautiful necklace.

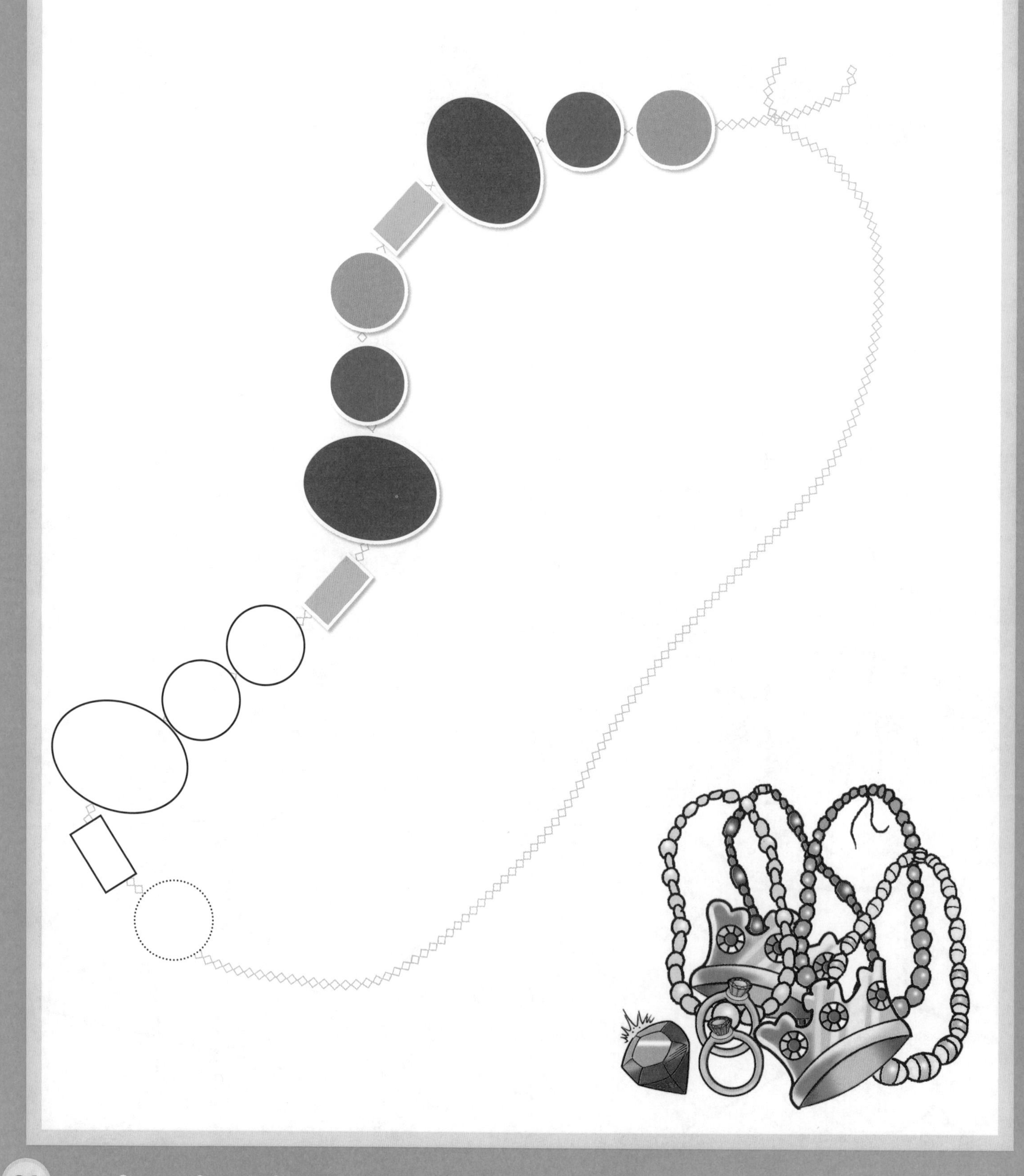

Circle the words that rhyme in each row.

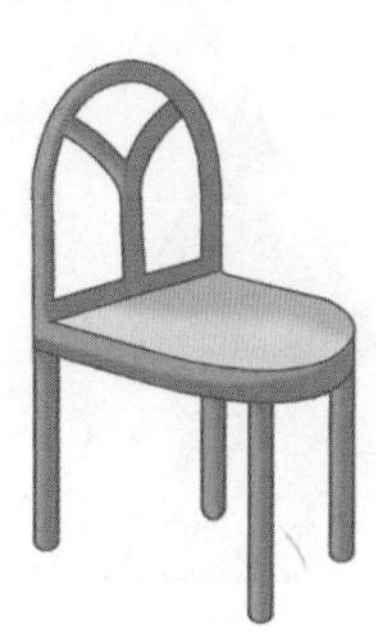

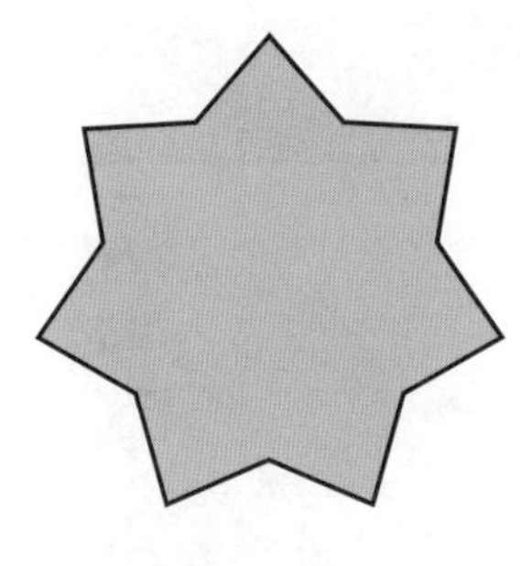

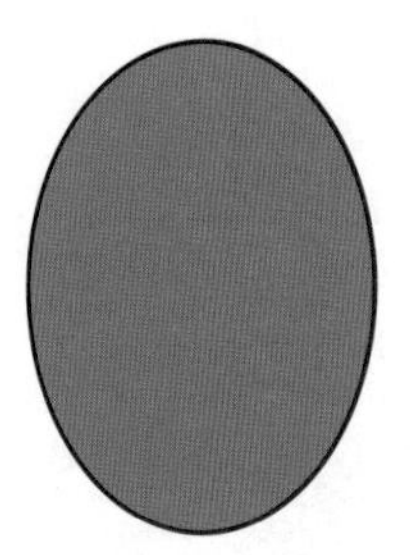

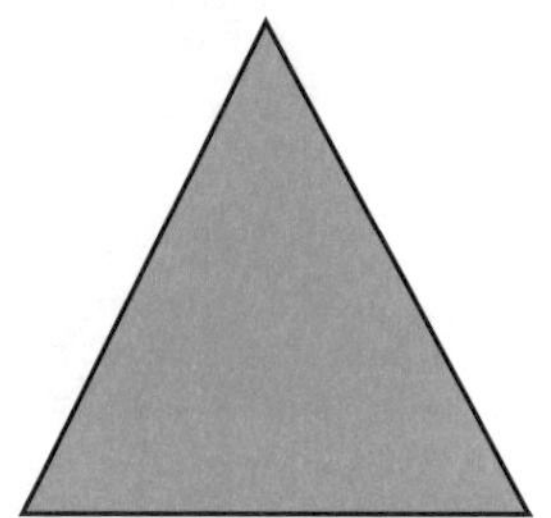

Sudoku! Draw in the last two shapes so that each shape only appears once in each row or column.

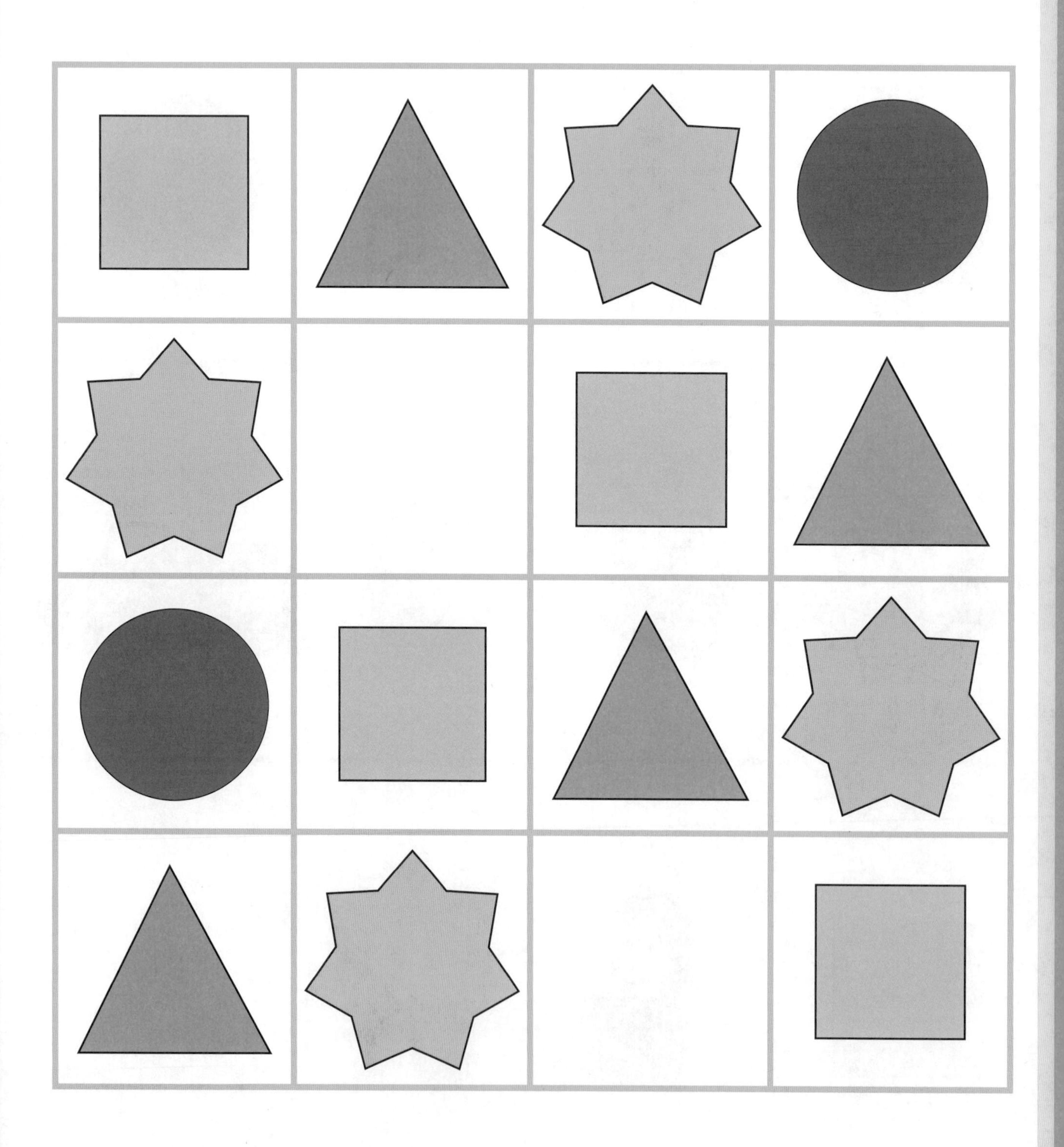

Listen and put a tick next to the matching picture.
The first one has been done for you.

Let's check!

1.  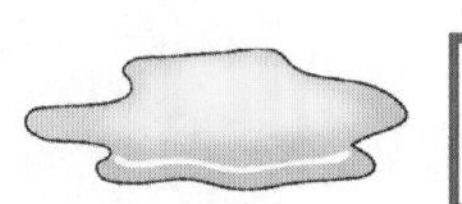  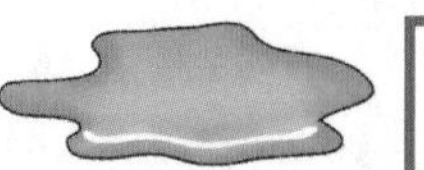 

2. 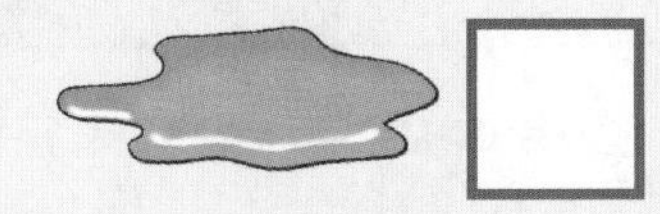 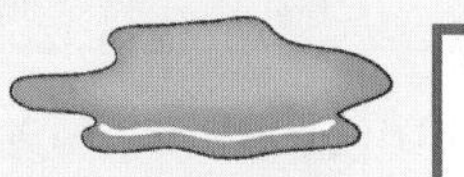  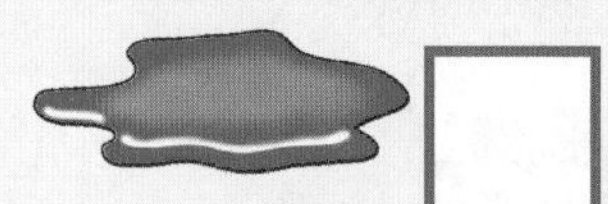

3. 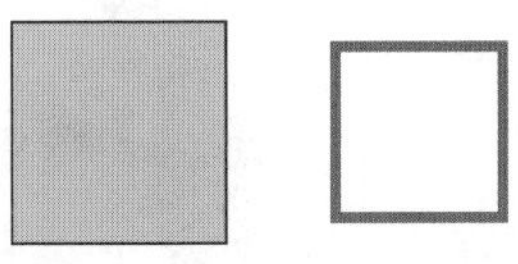 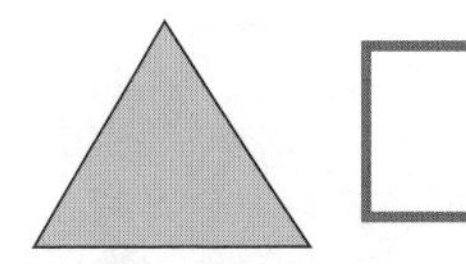 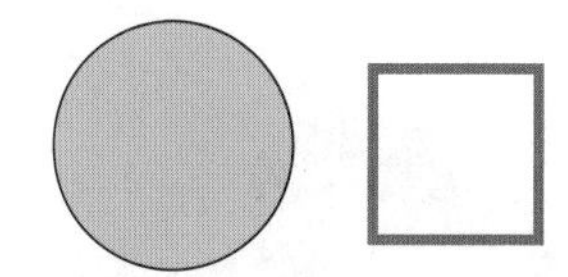

4. 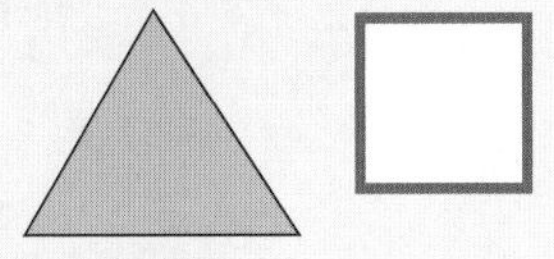 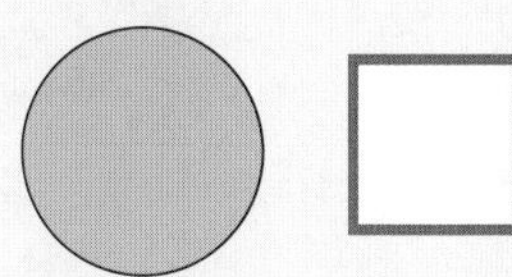 

5. 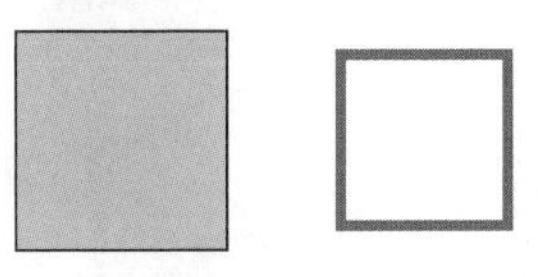 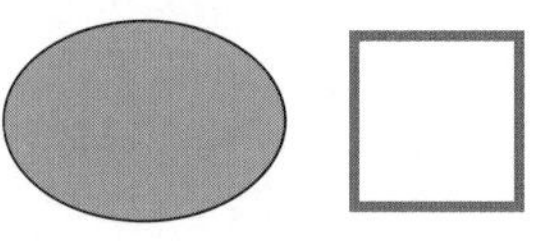 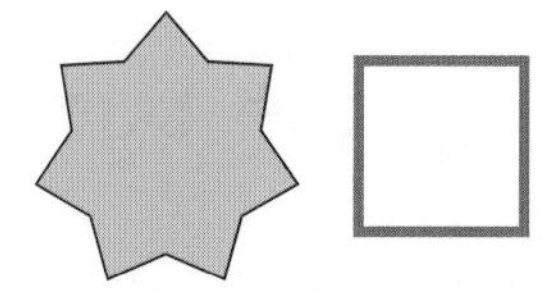

6. 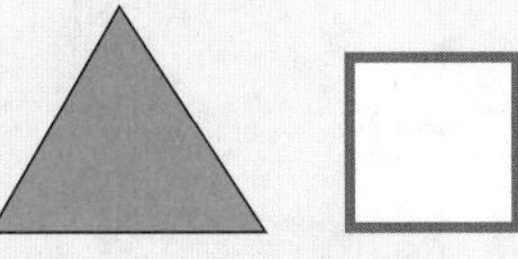 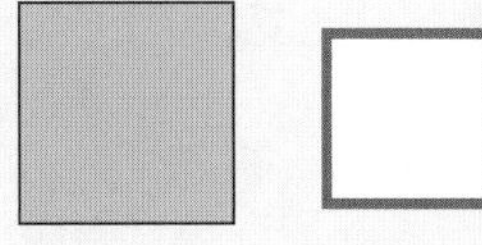 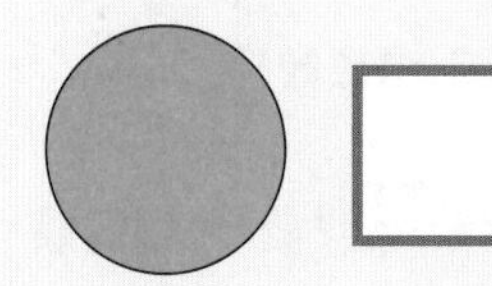

Decide whether you think your class is ready for this assessment. If it would be too challenging for individuals, simply move on or complete it as a group activity.

Action

Make waving movements with your hand and arm.
Do the action and say the rhythmic chant together!

Move and chant!

Let's wave, let's wave,

let's wave, good bye! (x 2)

Sing

Listen to the song first, then join in with just the '**Good bye**'.
Finally sing the whole song together.

Sing and move!

Good bye, good bye.

See you soon.

Bye bye, bye bye.

See you soon.

It's been fun.

We'll see you soon.

Good bye, good bye from Letterland!

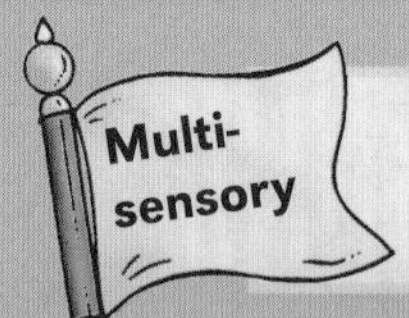

Children develop their communication skills by listening and singing along to songs. You might want to sing this song at the end of every lesson.